fimbles ™

I can feel a twinkling,

I can hear a sound,

It's telling me there's something

Waiting to be found!

Where is it?

Where is it?

What could it be?

I think it might be over there,

Let's go and see!

Fimbo   Florrie   Baby Pom

This Annual belongs to

. . . .

First published in 2003 by BBC Worldwide Limited
Woodlands, 80 Wood Lane, London W12 0TT
2 4 6 8 10 9 7 5 3 1
Written and adapted by Sarah O'Neill
'Makes' devised by Susan Jackman
Illustrations by Jenny Tulip
Photography on pages 10-11, 28-29, 38-39, 52-53 by Christopher Baines
With thanks to Caitlin, Boji and Tyler
Designed by Smiljka Surla
Fimbles ™ BBC

Fimbles is produced by Novel for BBC/BBC Worldwide Limited

Printed in Singapore

ISBN 0 563 49110 8

Bessie and
Ribble

Roly Mo

Rockit

4

Find out what's inside...

Can you find things like the Fimbles do? The objects below are all in your Annual. Which pages are they on? The answers are on page 61.

mouse

tambourine

cow

Wooden Spoon

FLORRIE was hopping on one foot and counting, "One, two, three..."

She started hopping on the other foot.

Baby Pom came to watch.

Florrie jumped, "One, two, three..."

"Pom, jump!" said Baby Pom.

"OK, Pom, but you've got to do everything three times," said Florrie.

Baby Pom tried, "One, one, three, one..."

"Let's try dancing, instead. One, two, three..." said Florrie.

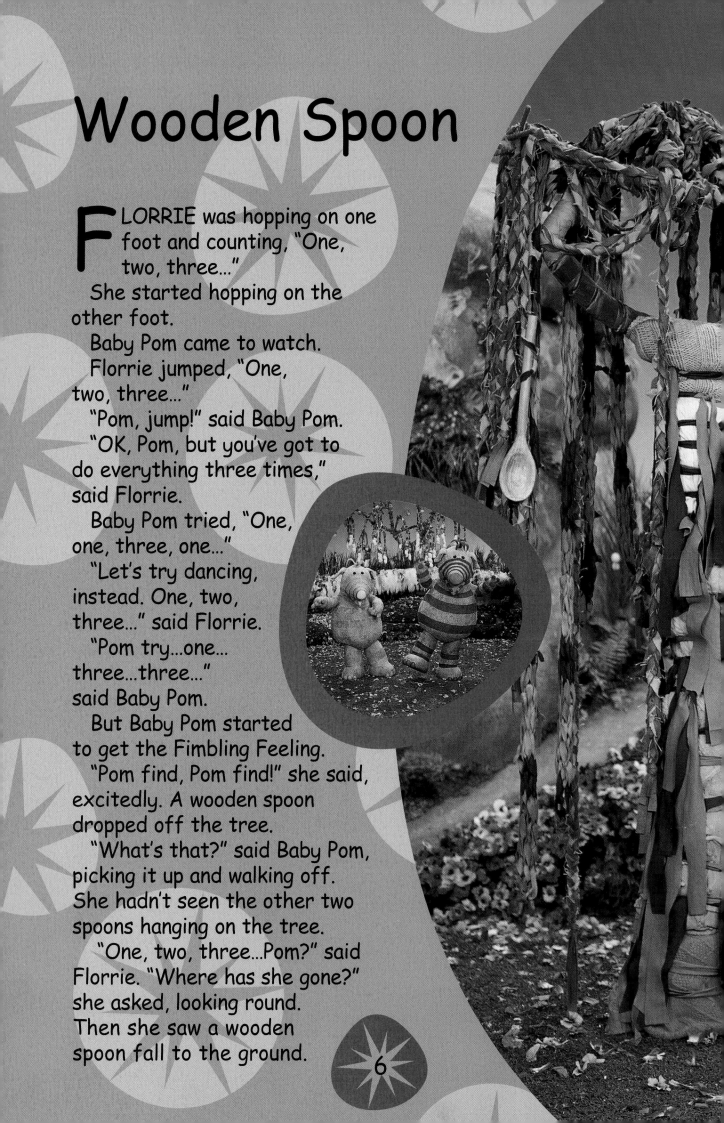

"Pom try...one... three...three..." said Baby Pom.

But Baby Pom started to get the Fimbling Feeling.

"Pom find, Pom find!" she said, excitedly. A wooden spoon dropped off the tree.

"What's that?" said Baby Pom, picking it up and walking off. She hadn't seen the other two spoons hanging on the tree.

"One, two, three...Pom?" said Florrie. "Where has she gone?" she asked, looking round. Then she saw a wooden spoon fall to the ground.

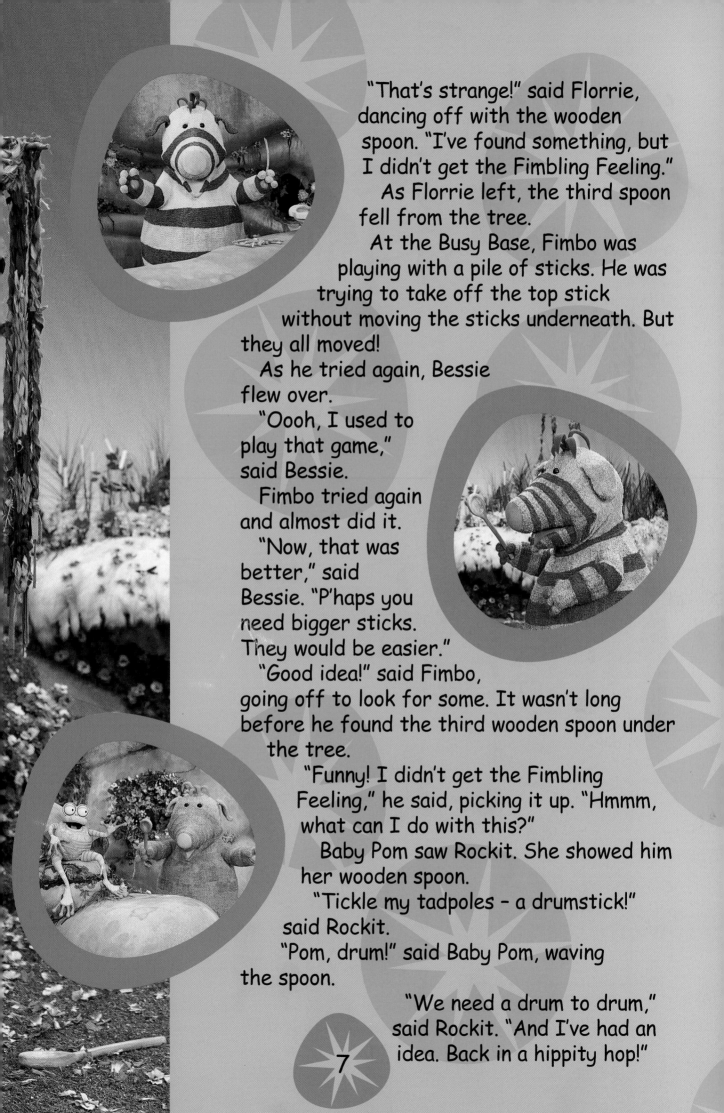

"That's strange!" said Florrie, dancing off with the wooden spoon. "I've found something, but I didn't get the Fimbling Feeling."

As Florrie left, the third spoon fell from the tree.

At the Busy Base, Fimbo was playing with a pile of sticks. He was trying to take off the top stick without moving the sticks underneath. But they all moved!

As he tried again, Bessie flew over.

"Oooh, I used to play that game," said Bessie.

Fimbo tried again and almost did it.

"Now, that was better," said Bessie. "P'haps you need bigger sticks. They would be easier."

"Good idea!" said Fimbo, going off to look for some. It wasn't long before he found the third wooden spoon under the tree.

"Funny! I didn't get the Fimbling Feeling," he said, picking it up. "Hmmm, what can I do with this?"

Baby Pom saw Rockit. She showed him her wooden spoon.

"Tickle my tadpoles – a drumstick!" said Rockit.

"Pom, drum!" said Baby Pom, waving the spoon.

"We need a drum to drum," said Rockit. "And I've had an idea. Back in a hippity hop!"

7

Meanwhile, Florrie was making a pretend cake for Ribble and Little One with her wooden spoon. She pretended to mix the cake in a bowl and then bake it.

"Are you hungry?" she asked, as she handed out pretend pieces of cake.

Baby Pom was tapping on her Trundle Truck when Rockit came back.

"Pom, look!" he said, holding up a cracker barrel. "A drum!"

Baby Pom started to tap it with her wooden spoon.

Roly Mo and Bessie came to see what all the noise was.

Then Fimbo and Florrie arrived with their wooden spoons.

They all showed Roly Mo their wooden spoons. Baby Pom drummed on the cracker barrel, and Florrie made pretend cake for everyone.

"Can I borrow your spoons, please?" said Fimbo. "I have a game to show you."

"Oooh, what's the game?" asked Rockit.

"You have to try
to take off the spoon on
top of the pile without
moving all the others," explained
Fimbo, lifting up the top spoon.
"Look, Bessie, I can do it now!"
"Well done!" said Bessie.
"Spoons one, two, three,"
said Pom, counting them.
"Well done, Pom!" said everyone.

The End

Wooden Spoon Fimbles

You will need:
three wooden spoons
paints
paintbrushes
pencil
felt or coloured card
safe glue
sticky tape
strips of ribbon
round-ended scissors

1 Paint the back of each wooden spoon a different colour, and add stripes like on the Fimbles' faces.

2 Use black paint to make eyes, and coloured paint for the noses.

3 Cut ears out of felt or coloured card, using the picture below as a guide, and glue them onto the spoons. Tape the ribbons to the tops of the spoons.

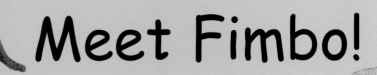

Meet Fimbo!

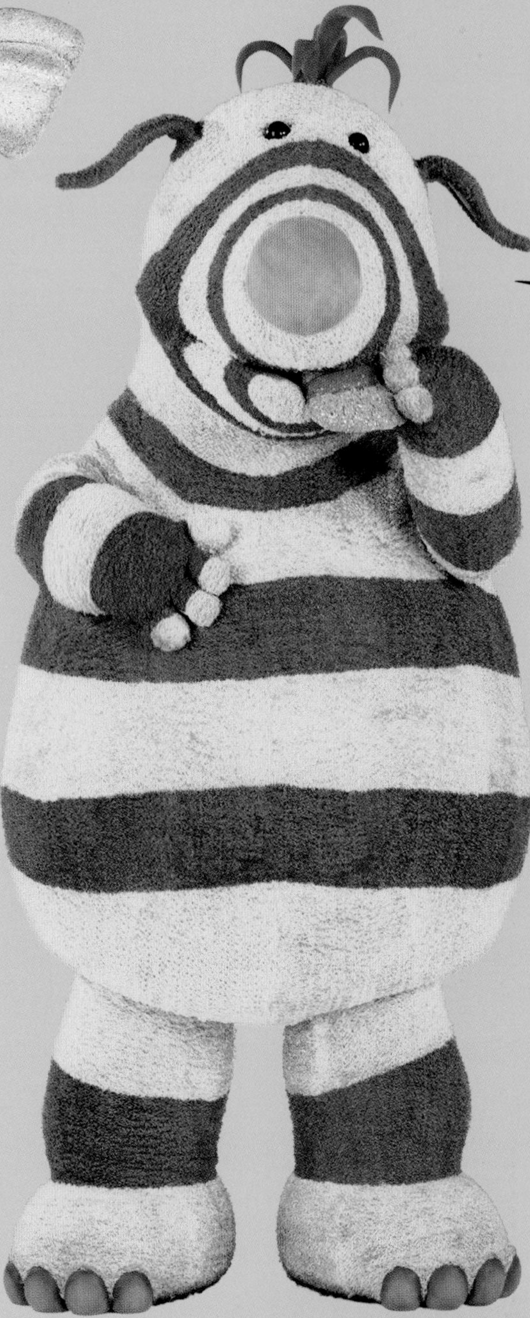
Hello! I'm Fimbo and I love Crumble Crackers, apples and finding things!

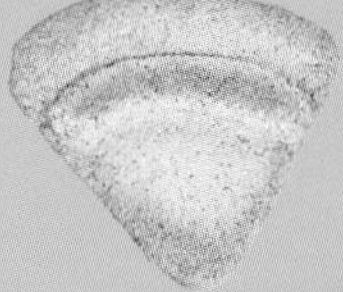

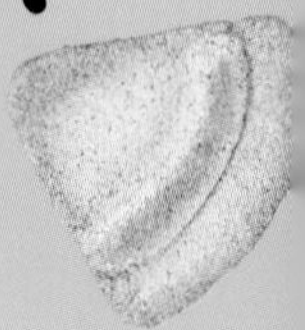

How many Crumble Crackers can you find on this page for Fimbo?

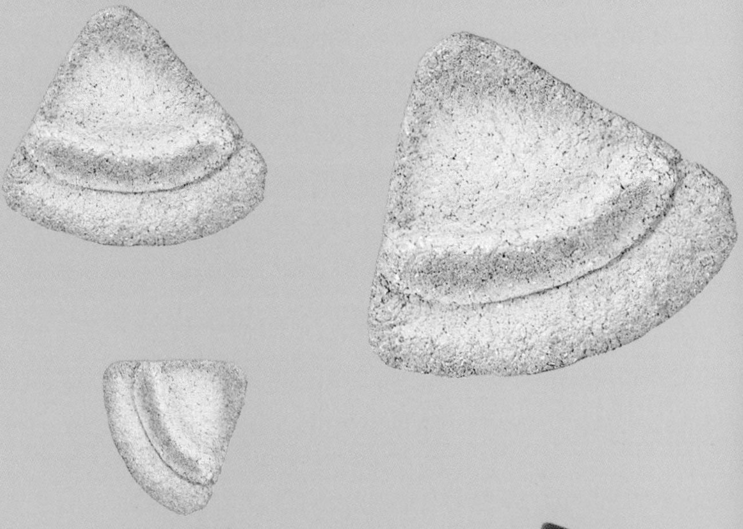

Fimbo also loves his Shimmy Shaker.

One of the Shimmy Shakers below is different. Can you spot the odd one out?

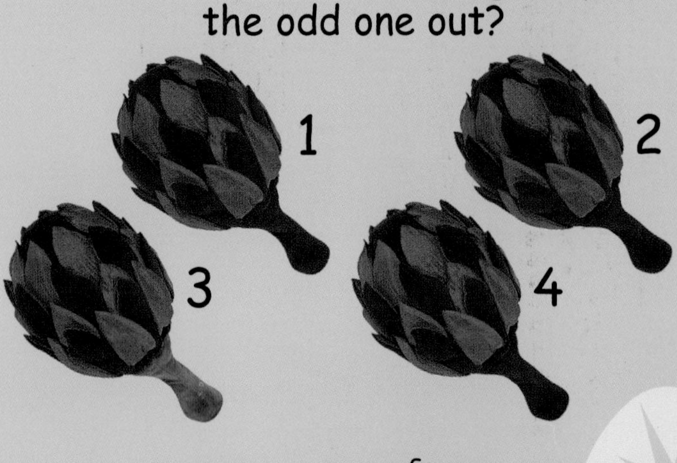
1
2
3
4

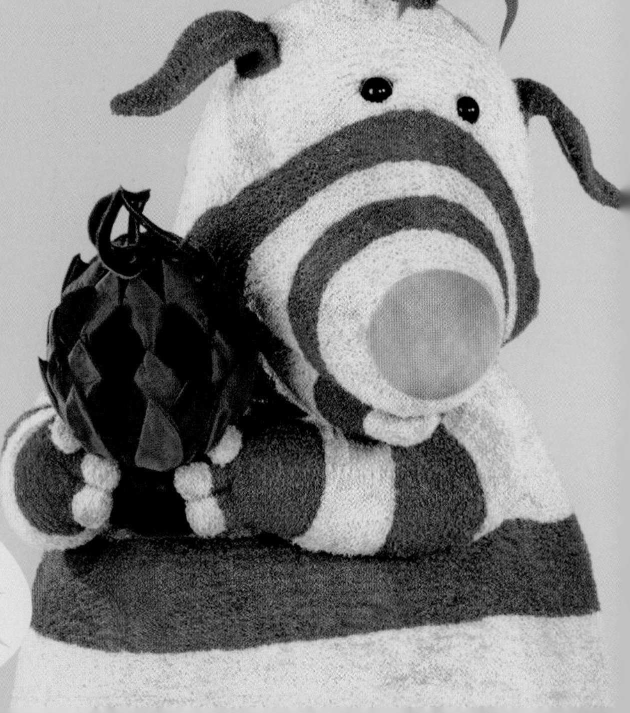

Answers: There are 5 Crumble Crackers. Shimmy Shaker 3 is different.

Colour in Fimbo

Sing Along!

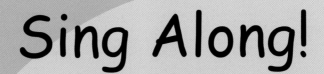

Sing this song to the tune of "Heads, Shoulders, Knees and Toes".

Point to your ears, eyes, mouth and nose as you sing!

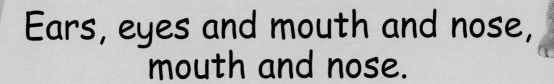

Ears, eyes and mouth and nose, mouth and nose.

Ears, eyes and mouth and nose, mouth and nose.

They make a face and this is how it goes!

Ears, eyes and mouth and nose, mouth and nose.

Rhyming Words

Draw lines to match each pair of rhyming words below.

cat

dish

cake

lock

fish

hat

sock

bake

15

Meet Florrie!

Hello! I'm Florrie and I like to play with my doll, Little One.

How many apples can you find on this page for Florrie?

Trace the lines with your finger to lead Florrie to Little One.

Answer: There are 3 apples.

Colour in Florrie

Maze

Help the Fimbles through the maze.
How many crackers and apples can
you find along the way?

Start

Finish

Answers: There are 4 crackers
and 5 apples to find along the way.

What Comes Next?

Look at these rows of pictures.
Draw what comes next in the boxes
and write over the dotted words.

keys   shoe   keys   shoe

hairbrush   book   hairbrush   book

duck   box   duck   box

Meet Baby Pom!

Pom, Pom!
Play, play!

How many flowers can you find
on this page for Baby Pom?

Baby Pom's favourite
thing is her
Trundle Truck.

Draw something below
to go in it.

20

Answer: There are 9 flowers.

Colour in Baby Pom

21

Spot the Difference

How many differences can you find between
these two pictures?

I found ⬤ differences.

Answers: There are 4 differences.
In the second picture, Bessie, Ribble and an
apple have been added, and Fimbo is holding
some flowers.

What Did You Find?

Here's a chart for you to fill in
about different things that you find.
Fimbo's shown you how to fill it in!

1	**What did you find?** Write or draw it here. I found a leaf.	**Describe it here.** It's green and shiny and comes from a tree.
2		
3		
4		

24

Fimbo's Picture Frame

Find a photograph of yourself and stick it into Fimbo's picture frame. Don't forget to colour in the border, too!

Ask a grown-up to help choose a photograph of you, then carefully stick it here with safe glue.

Meet Rockit!

Smelly jelly!
I like the Fimbles, bouncing,
and telling jokes!

Can you think of a joke to tell Rockit?

. . . .

. . . .

. . . .

Which words would you use to
describe Rockit?

quiet

friendly

funny

sad

happy

Answers: Rockit is
funny, friendly
and happy.

Colour in Rockit

Make Rockit

You will need:
tracing paper, red, white and pale blue card, pencil, round-ended scissors, safe glue, paints, paintbrush.

1 Put the tracing paper over the templates and trace a head, body, two legs and two arms in pencil. Turn over the paper and scribble over the lines on the back. Put the paper the right way up on the pale blue card. Pressing hard on the pencil, draw over the lines.

2 Cut out the pieces and fold along the dotted lines. Put glue above the dotted line on the body. Stick the head on top of the body, making sure the lower dotted line on the head is on top of the dotted line on the body. Stick on Rockit's arms and legs.

28

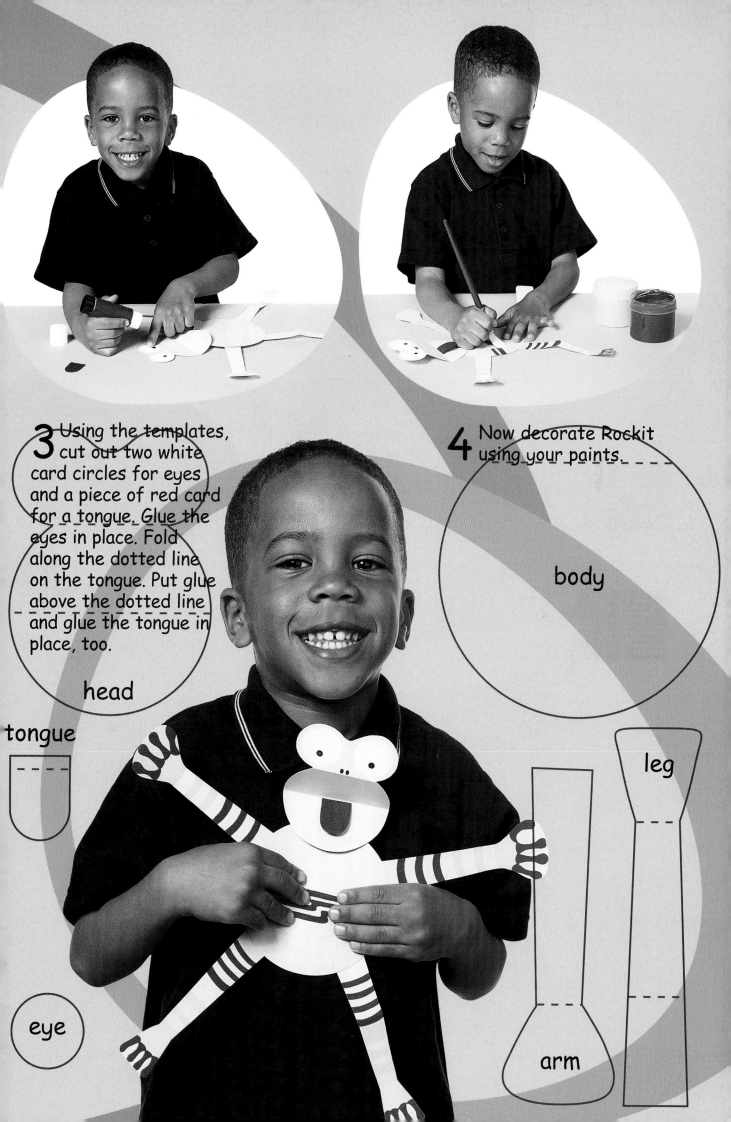

3 Using the templates, cut out two white card circles for eyes and a piece of red card for a tongue. Glue the eyes in place. Fold along the dotted line on the tongue. Put glue above the dotted line and glue the tongue in place, too.

head

tongue

eye

4 Now decorate Rockit using your paints.

body

leg

arm

What Can You See?

Look at the big picture and
answer the questions.

What do you think the Fimbles have found?

How many Fimbles can you see?

What colours are the Trundle Truck?

Point to Roly Mo.

Can you find Rockit in the big picture?

Answers: The Fimbles have found a hooter. There are 3 Fimbles. The Trundle Truck is yellow and red. Roly Mo is on the right of the picture, and Rockit is just above Florrie.

Odd One Out

Look carefully at these pictures of the
Fimbles' Busy Box.
Can you spot the odd one out?

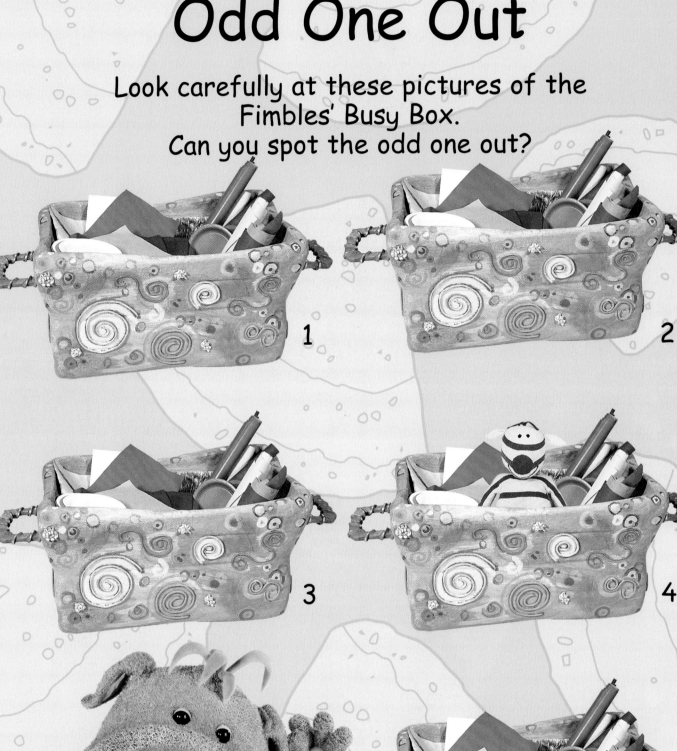

1

2

3

4

5

Answer: 4 is the odd one out.

Follow the Lines

Find out what each Fimble has found, by carefully following the lines with your finger or a pencil.

book　　　　　duck　　　　　shoe

Snowflake

FLORRIE was at the Busy Base with Little One, deciding what to make.

"I've got lots of sparkly things," she said, waving some silver tinsel.

Fimbo and Baby Pom were in the Purple Meadow, playing the 'piece of string' game. Fimbo held out both hands, tightly closed.

"Piece of string, piece of string, which hand is it in?" he said.

"String!" said Baby Pom, tapping one of Fimbo's hands.

Fimbo opened his hand slowly and there was the string! They kept playing until Baby Pom grabbed the piece of string and ran off towards the Happy Hollow. She hid the string behind the arch, giggling to herself.

All of a sudden, she had a Fimbly Bimbly Feeling. She ran into the Happy Hollow and, when she looked up, something small and white came spinning down towards her.

"Shiny! Sparkle!" she said, and grabbed it. But when she opened her hand, there was nothing there!

"Where gone?" she asked.

Catching another shiny, sparkly thing, Baby Pom closed her hand tightly and went to show Fimbo. Fimbo was in the Comfy Corner.

"Fimbo, look!" said Baby Pom. But when she opened her hand, there was nothing there!

"Is it in the other hand, Pom?" asked Fimbo.

"Oh, gone again!" said Baby Pom, looking for it. She looked up and saw another shiny, sparkly thing.

"Ah, look, look!" she giggled.
She caught it in her hand again,
making sure her hand was safely closed.
Baby Pom went to find Florrie, who
was dressing Little One in tinsel.
"Hello, Pom. What have you found?"
asked Florrie.
Baby Pom slowly opened her
hand...nothing!
"What did you find, Pom? I can't see
anything," said Florrie.
Bessie flew over. "Did someone find something?"
Just then, there was a sudden flurry of the shiny, sparkly things.
"Is this what you found, Pom?" laughed Bessie.

"Es!" said Baby Pom.

Bessie explained that sometimes, when it's really cold, it snows. But when it gets warmer, the snowflakes melt away. The snow flurry was stopping.

"Oh, snow gone again!" said Baby Pom sadly.

"We can make our very own snowflakes," said Florrie, fetching some white paper.

Florrie folded a piece of paper over a few times.

"Now we rip it," said Florrie, tearing the paper. When she unfolded it, she had made a pretty paper snowflake. Baby Pom made snowflakes by tearing her paper into tiny pieces.

"Pom snowflakes!" said Baby Pom.

Florrie giggled. "Now I can put some sparkly glitter on my snowflake!" she said.

Florrie dabbed her snowflake with glue and sprinkled glitter over it. She and Baby Pom held their snowflakes up to show Bessie.

Rockit was bouncing up and down on a rock, when a snowflake landed on his nose!

"Glung! What's that? It's very cold!" he said, wriggling his nose. "Well, tickle my tadpoles, it's snowing in Fimble Valley. I must tell the others!" He hopped away.

Roly Mo stuck his head out of his hole and sniffed the air.

"Hmmmm, it smells like snow," he said. "What fun!"

Rockit hopped over. "Guess what, Roly?"

"It's snowing, Rockit!" said Roly Mo.

Florrie and Baby Pom were playing in the Purple Meadow when Fimbo came along.

"It's snowing!" said Fimbo, excitedly.
"We know, Fimbo! Pom found a snowflake. And then we made our own snowflakes," said Florrie, holding hers up.
"Oh, it's stopped," said Fimbo.
Roly Mo came along and read them a story about a snowflake. Florrie told Roly Mo about the snowflakes they'd made. Then the Fimbles sang a song about snowflakes.
"I'm a little snowflake, see me swirl,
I twirl and I swirl and I dance around,
then I float down to the ground.
A snowflake sparkles and it's ever so white,
a snowflake sparkles and it shines in the light,
a snowflake is wet and it doesn't last long,
you hold it in your hand and then it's gone."
Baby Pom looked up to the sky and pointed.
"Look!" she said.
"Hooray," cried everyone. "It's snowing again!"

The End

Glittery Hat

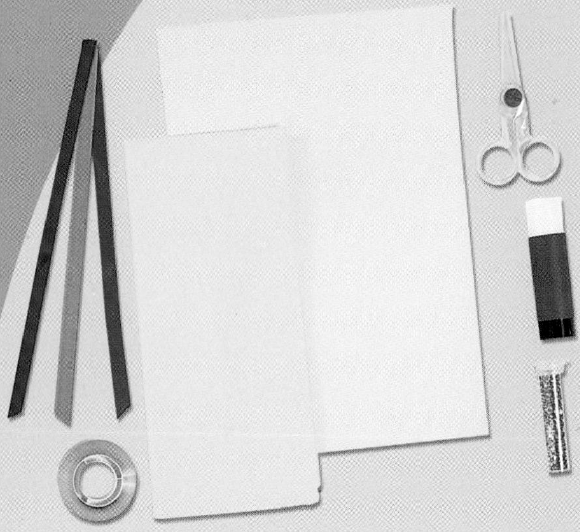

You will need:
coloured card
round-ended scissors
sticky tape
safe glue
glitter
strips of ribbon

1 Cut a semi-circle from a piece of coloured card.

2 Roll the paper into a cone shape and tape the edges together.

3 Decorate your hat with sparkly glitter and stick ribbons to the top.

Meet Roly Mo!

I'm Roly Mo and I like to read stories and rhymes to the Fimbles!

Tell Roly Mo your favourite story or rhyme!

Now sing Roly Mo's song!

When you take a look inside a book,
who knows what you might see.
A story or rhyme,
just take the time,
to read along with me!

Colour in Roly Mo

Blue

THE Fimbles were playing hide-and-seek.

"I'll hide first," said Fimbo.

"One, two, three," began Florrie as Fimbo went to hide in the Playdips.

When suddenly...

"I'm getting the Fimbling Feeling!" said Fimbo.

He twirled round and round, and came to a stop.

He saw something sparkling and shimmering in the Funpuddle.

"It's not a puddle – it's blue!" he said.

Fimbo carefully dipped a stick into the blue, but didn't notice when he lifted it out, that some dripped onto the ground.

"I think the others would like to see this!" he said.

As he left, Fimbo stepped in the blue.

He left a trail of blue footprints behind him.

When he got to the Comfy Corner, Fimbo's nose began to twitch.

"I can smell crackers," he said and ate the last two crackers out of the cracker barrel.

"Look!" called Baby Pom, pointing to something blue on the ground.

"What is it?" asked Florrie.

"A piece of sky?" suggested Rockit.

"It's a footprint," laughed Florrie.

"This could be the footprint of the Blue Galoo!" said Rockit.

Bessie flew in to take a look.

"If you follow the footprints, you might just find out," she smiled.

So off they went in search of the Blue Galoo.

The footprints led them all the way to the Comfy Corner.

"Look!" said Florrie, pointing at the empty cracker barrel. "The Blue Galoo has eaten all our crackers."

Meanwhile, Fimbo had walked in a big circle back to the Funpuddle.

"Look at those!" he said, looking at the footprints on the ground.

Fimbo had followed the footprints round the Playdips when he bumped into Florrie, Baby Pom and Rockit.

"You! Blue Galoo!" said Baby Pom, pointing at Fimbo's feet.

"Oh, so you ate all the crackers!" said Florrie.

"I'm sorry, I was hungry," Fimbo explained.

"I wonder what a real Blue Galoo looks like," said Florrie.

"Whatever you want it to," said Roly Mo.

"Look," said Fimbo, as he poked his paintbrush into the Funpuddle and dropped a blob of blue onto a piece of paper. He folded the paper in half.

"There!" he said, opening the paper. "It's my very own Blue Galoo!"

The End

Read and Find

The Fimbles are thinking about things they've found. When you've guessed which thing they're describing, point to it!

"You use these when you sneeze!"

"Squeak, Squeak!"

"You wear this
on your foot!"

tissues

shoe

mouse

Answers: You use tissues when you sneeze.
A mouse squeaks. You wear a shoe on
your foot.

Colour in the Fimbles and their Friends

Rockit's Jokes!

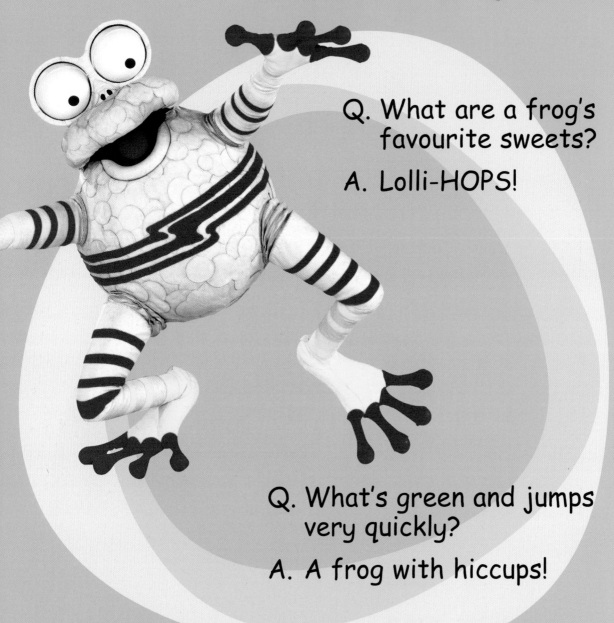

Q. What are a frog's favourite sweets?

A. Lolli-HOPS!

Q. What's green and jumps very quickly?

A. A frog with hiccups!

Q. What's a frog's favourite game?

A. HOP-scotch!

Q. What did the bus driver
   say to the frog?

A. HOP on!

Q. Which is a frog's
   favourite year?

A. A LEAP year!

Q. Where do frogs
   keep their money?

A. In a river bank!

Now tell a friend your favourite
Rockit joke!

Meet Bessie and Ribble!

Hello, my little chickadees! I'm Bessie and this is my little darling, Ribble. Nice to meet you!

Help Bessie through the maze to reach Rockit. Don't forget to collect Ribble along the way!

Colour in Bessie and Ribble

Pom-Pom Ribble

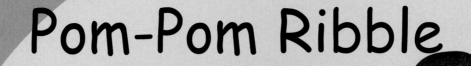

You will need:
bright orange wool
safe glue
round-ended scissors
white card
pencil

1 Draw two circles on card and cut them out. Ask a grown-up to help you cut a smaller circle from the centre of each one.

2 Place the two circles together. Cut lengths of bright orange wool and, passing it through the hole, wrap the wool around the card.

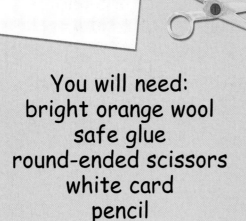

3 When the card is covered with layers of wool, ask a grown-up to help you push the scissors in between the two circles of card. Then cut through the wool, all the way around the outside circle.

5 Now pat the pom-pom into shape. Finally, cut out a beak from a piece of white card and glue it in place.

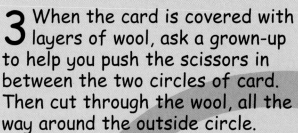

4 When you have finished cutting, tie a piece of wool firmly between the two pieces of card and then carefully remove the cardboard circles.

What's Missing?

hooter

cow

duck

book

hairbrush

shoe

Look carefully at these two circles of things the Fimbles have found. What's missing from the second circle?

shoe

book

hairbrush

hooter

duck

Answer: The cow is missing.

Who's Hiding?

Roly Mo

Florrie

Fimbo

Can you guess who's hiding behind these flowers?
Look at the pictures at the bottom of
these pages to help you!

Bessie and
Ribble

Rockit

Baby Pom

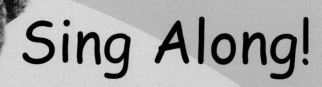

Sing Along!

Sing this song and do the actions!

If you're happy and you know it
clap your hands.
If you're happy and you know it
clap your hands.
If you're happy and you know it
and you really want to show it,
if you're happy and you know
it clap your hands.

If you're happy and you
know it jump up high.
If you're happy and you know it
jump up high.
If you're happy and you know it
and you really want to show it,
if you're happy and you know it
jump up high.

Think of another action for this
song. Then sing another verse and
do the actions.

58

What's Hiding?

There are lots of things hidden around the Tinkling Tree. Help the Fimbles find them.

Can You Remember?

Have you finished looking through your Annual?
Look at these questions with Roly Mo, Bessie and
Ribble and see what you can remember.

1. How many spoons did the Fimbles find in
the 'Wooden Spoon' story?

Write the number in the box.

2. Does Rockit like to bounce?

Tick the right box below.

yes   no

3. What did Florrie use to make a snowflake in the
'Snowflake' story?

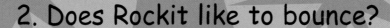

4. Circle Baby Pom's favourite thing.

Little One   book   Trundle Truck

5. Fimbo doesn't like Crumble Crackers.

Tick the right box below.

☐ true　　　☐ false

6. Does Little One belong to Florrie or Ribble?

. . . .

7. What other food do the Fimbles like, besides Crumble Crackers?

Draw it here.

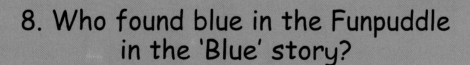

8. Who found blue in the Funpuddle in the 'Blue' story?

. . . .

The Finding Game

Now it's your turn to pretend to be one of the Fimbles, in this game for three players.

You will need a die and some counters.
Decide which of you is Fimbo, who is Florrie, and who is Baby Pom.
The winner is the Fimble who gets to the Finish first!
Don't forget to sing the Fimbles' finding song whenever you find something along the way.

Rockit wants to
show you a flower.
Bounce back 3
spaces with him.

You find a star!
Move forward
3 spaces.

You stop to
eat an apple.
Miss a turn.

Start